Concrete Is Not Always Hard

Concrete Is Not Always Hard

by A. Barbara Pilon

Xerox Education Publications

To Al,
  Alice,
    Frank,
      and John
who have always made it so easy

Copyright © 1972 by A. Barbara Pilon

Publishing, Executive, and Editorial Offices:
Xerox Education Publications
Middletown, Connecticut 06457

Library of Congress Card Catalogue No. 72–83536

2 3 4 5/76 75 74 73

Contents

Note to Teachers:
In the Beginning
☐ ☐ ☐ ☐ ☐ ☐ ☐ ☐ ☐ ☐

Not so terribly long ago, not much longer than a few yesterdays ago, if a teacher mentioned the word "poetry" to young people, unfortunately, unpleasant thoughts spontaneously sprang up in their minds. A great number of students groaned inwardly, if not outwardly, at what seemed certain to follow. And there was no physical escape route for them. All of a sudden stereotyped, narrow ideas, tight topics, and words loomed up out of a language closet for which they wished they had a permanent lock.

If the subject of poetry was brought up, too many students felt that they were going to be compelled to be "serious." Many, too many, received the "depression" that they were going to be expected to say or write something profound and symbolic. Along with this, they somehow knew that whatever *they* wanted to express would never be considered profound or symbolic enough or what the teacher wanted. They usually were conditioned to expect a mark (a "mock"?) for their contributions or maybe even a helpful comment such as "missed the point entirely." More dreaded than these prospects was the fear that they might receive their papers back with the terrible words "write over" on them. For some students surely the temptation must have come at one time or another to do literally what their teacher suggested—"write over" what they had already passed in. Such students must have learned from past experience that "writing over" would make little or no difference in their teacher's judgment of the value of their work. Theirs was simply an exercise in futility.

The "righting" approach to writing and poetry understandably was responsible for producing many negative attitudes in children toward poetry. The "righting" approach to poetry was, in reality, a "wronging" approach to both poetry and young people. Surely, causing students to dislike poetry could not have been any teacher's conscious objective when she used poetry in the ways which have just been described. But this definitely was the result. Of course, all of this took place yesterdays ago.

Luckily, in the world of now when the topic of poetry comes up, most young people do not think automatically of words such as "Moon" and "June." Fortunately, they do not feel it necessary to deck themselves out with all the good luck charms they possess in the hope of warding off the evil prospects of listening to poetry they neither like nor understand. They do not feel it is inevitable that they are going to be required to tell or write about how crocuses feel in the spring or where they would like to fall if they were a dewdrop—and all within a rigidly set word and/or line prison with no options offered.

Today readers are not made to feel that they must "do" something with a poem if they so much as glance at it. They do not get the sneaking suspicion that reading a poem naturally means that they then must reveal the mysteries of what "blankety blank" meant when he said "blankety blank."

Readers of *Concrete Is Not Always Hard*, happily, may discover kinds of poems that are entirely new to them. This in itself is a plus factor. There are poems in this anthology that they can look at, laugh at, listen to. linger over, or leave. That's one nice thing about a book: sections of it may be left out or skipped lightly over, and yet a book will never hold it against the reader. The reader is the one who does the holding up and the folding up, and that is just as it should be.

There should be no specific poems in this book, or in any other book, for that matter, that students *have* to read or *have* to do something with. The readers should be the masters of any book.

It seems as though having to do anything somehow takes the joy out of the doing. And making students do something with poetry is not the way teachers can bring poetry and young people together. People need to be given the opportunity to make choices, to decide whether something appeals to them and to be able to express their views honestly without being penalized for doing so. Because everyone is an individual, there should be more than one idea a teacher could supply and use with a group of students who seem particularly excited about any selection to keep their own thoughts on fire. A teacher, too, should actively encourage students' own thinking on various works in the book and use their imaginative ideas as springboards into their own creative inner spaces. By employing this technique a teacher can help the youngsters' creativity surface.

Of course, this all implies that a teacher is a person who listens to students and can respond to what is heard. It implies that the teacher will encourage students to talk freely and spontaneously about a major or minor idea blizzard which a poem has started in their minds and spirits. A teacher should tell students about some of his or her own idea buds that have been piqued into being by poems read. The teacher should try to give his or her own idea buds and the students' buds a free and easy outlet and then let them take shape, grow, and blossom. The important point is to get them out. The first form the ideas take does not matter. The final form may not resemble the first in the least. The final form does not matter either. That is, a student may start out thinking he or she is going to write an essay but the idea may end up as a poem.

A teacher should talk and write along with students—should let them know what he or she is thinking and playing with and attempting to convey. Teacher and students should be active and growing participants in the learning process. A teacher who travels with students creates quite a different atmosphere in the classroom than one who simply gives route directions but never goes along on the trip herself. Every teacher should try to be a tugger of his or her own mind strings as well as those of the students. But the teacher must always remember that, in addition to being a mind-string tugger, he or she must be a heart-tugger also. Otherwise, the songs produced in the students will be in a minor key only. The secret of being a major-type teacher is to help children find joy in learning.

A Few Concrete Suggestions for Using This Book with Students
☐☐☐☐☐☐☐☐☐☐☐☐☐☐☐☐☐☐☐☐☐

It is evident, as one looks through this book, that there are many poems written on the same subject. For instance, there are several number poems where the authors play around with the sounds of words. Included are two number poems by Eve Merriam. The purpose of these two poems is to show that quite often authors get another writing idea from something they have. already produced. Additionally, one author will read another author's work and it will spark the beginnings of a writing of his or her own invention. Many different poems may be found in this anthology that are written on the same subject. The reader will find, for example, more than one poem included about lollipops, icicles, Christmas trees, and flowers. I think that as a teacher I would point this out to students since there may still be some who feel that there can be only one response to any given stimulus. And they may think that one response to be the "correct" response. In this book they can see a rich divergence and fluency of ideas derived from one source.

A teacher can encourage students, with her guidance, to play around with words and space and sounds to create their own lollipop, icicle, Christmas tree, and flower poems. She can suggest other stimuli for them to respond to also. Rather than expecting each person to create a work (which is quite threatening), it is wiser to work, at least initially, with the youngsters in a group effort, accepting volunteered responses and changes the group decides to make. Young people must have choices and ample time to think and the opportunity to tear their papers up if they want to, or do nothing if they want to, on what has been suggested.

A teacher using a poem in this book, such as Regina Sauro's "I Like to Swing," working together with those who might be interested, could ask how else an author might space her words so that it would look as though a person were actually swinging. How might an author indicate that first one would start out close to the ground and then, gradually, as he or she gained more and more momentum soon would be soaring? The teacher could ask helpful questions to get the students talking and discussing such as: Do you think the beginning lines should be short? What about the middle lines? the ending lines? What words might you use to let someone know how you would feel when you were swinging high above the ground? Could you use the spaces on your paper to show how near or far away you were from the ground? The teacher might then start recording some of their thoughts and changing them as they saw fit to make changes. Some children after this type of warm-up might want to work on their own ideas.

A poem such as May Swenson's "Cardinal Ideograms" could be discussed with students to see if they could come up with some ideas of their own for using the numbers one to ten. They could adapt Miss Swenson's idea, too, and instead of using numbers could take various letters of the alphabet and discuss what the letters make them think of.

Youngsters who are reluctant readers, as well as gifted students, may have fun with poems such as "Apfel" and "Individualista." They will need to look closely at both selections to see the points being made. There should be no reading strain since there are only two words involved in the first poem and none in the second—only a letter. The latter poem might prove to be a fine one for opening up a discussion on just what it does mean to be an individual. Both poems should make students chuckle. Poems that should do little other than cause the readers to laugh are "Fisches Nachtgesang" and "Night Song of the Fish." (Some things do get lost in translation, but very seldom is the losing as much fun as it is in the translation of this poem.)

In discussing these poems there can be no "right" or "wrong" answers, and therefore a student who may not have had the greatest success in reading or in language arts in general, as well as a brighter student, might find this very rewarding. These types of poems are the kind that can be used to develop children's language skills and fluency in a most delightful way.

Another poem which should be able to produce the same results as the ones just referred to is Eve Merriam's "Showers, Clearing Later in the Day." This is an example of a piece of poetry which uses no verbal language at all in its body. Some youngsters might want to retitle Miss Merriam's poem and use the same marks she uses and then later talk about what they meant by their poems.

There are many poems included in this anthology that contain very few words but say a great deal. For example, Mason Williams' "What's It All About?" and "I Don't Know" as well as Ian Hamilton Finlay's "Star" would appeal to readers of varying abilities. As every teacher knows, there is a wide reading range in any given grade level. So although the words are few in a great number of the poems selected for this anthology, the thoughts they may ignite are many.

A poem such as "His Thinking on Anything" might cause young people to want to describe orally people who could be categorized in the same way. Students could start talking about individuals they might know, either personally or indirectly, because of their exposure via various communication media. Some students might even want to write a short selection about a person's characteristics that would fit the title.

Because there are so many samples of concrete representations of single words in this book (as an illustration, look at "Fooling Around with Words") a teacher might want to try to use this technique to expand the vocabulary of some of the slower students as well as to invite some of the brighter students to think of other words they could illustrate concretely. Some suggestions for students to nibble on are provided in the section "For You to Try."

If students come up with different responses to the same stimuli, they should be reinforced in their divergent and appropriate thoughts. Of course, it would be wonderful for the teacher to make it possible for the class to see all of the various ideas resulting from the given stimuli as well as the creative responses which have resulted from the new stimuli they have come up with themselves. A teacher could provide word stimuli such as "love" and "hate," for example, and see the various concrete ways in which the students could interpret the given verbal symbols.

Two sources a teacher might want to consult to provide some more ideas for illustrating words concretely and writing concrete poems are *Talking Words: A Unique Alphabet Book* by Ashok Davor (The Bobbs-Merrill Co., Inc., Indianapolis, 1969) and "Concrete Poetry: Creative Writing for ALL Students" by Lavonne Mueller (*English Journal*, LVIII, October 1969, pp. 1053–1056).

Some students, if they are stimulated or encouraged, might want to tell and/or write about the way(s) in which they would rewrite a poem included in this anthology. For instance, a teacher might talk with some students about the various ways in which they might be able to reveal their feelings on life or silence. They might take a poem such as Eugen Gomringer's "Ping-Pong" and try to show exactly the plays in a specific Ping-Pong game. A teacher might ask: Did the ball come over the net fast or slow? High or low? Was the ball smashed down or swooped up? Responded to or missed? Different youngsters and the teacher then might begin writing the poem over again together so that the reader could "see" a particular game being played.

Introduction
□ □ □ □ □ □ □ □

"When I use a word," Humpty Dumpty said, in rather a scornful tone, "it means just what I choose it to mean—neither more nor less."

"The question is," said Alice, "whether you *can* make words mean so many different things."

"The question is," said Humpty Dumpty, "which is to be master —that's all."

Poetry is made up by people. People like you and me. They create the forms; they invent variations of the forms; they break rules; they make new ones. They are the *masters*. In this respect concrete poets are no different from any other poets. If they say something is something, it is—"that's all."

Who is a poet? Everyone is. However, sometimes we need to have others hear our inner voices so that we can receive confirmation and affirmation of our creative powers. Many of the selections in this book implicitly invite you to come along with the authors and be poets out loud.

In this anthology there are concrete poems written by people of your own age, poems written by teachers, poems written by me, and poems written by well-known poets. All of the writers' contributions are mixed together. The poems are just sitting, waiting, and hoping that they will be the ones that will beckon to your poetic voice to come out from wherever it is so that it can be seen, heard, felt, and discussed.

Have you ever thought of writing a poem using only a letter, a word, distortions of words, nonsense words, or no words at all? Have you ever thought of using the space around words to help the reader understand the idea you are trying to communicate? All these techniques are used by concrete poets.

With some concrete poems, nuances inherent in the poems and your interpretation of the poems will depend on the way *you* read them. Some concrete poets use no punctuation or standard capitalization or even standard line forms. You can read what they have presented right to left, left to right, down and up, up and down—

it all depends on you, the active participant in the poem.

Concrete poets sometimes make you see what they are saying in their works. That is, concrete poems sometimes take on the shape of the ideas the authors are trying to share with you.

Poets are language lovers and language players. Making poems is their game. In this anthology many poems are games designed for you, the player. When you have discovered the key to a poem, you may smile to yourself and say, "I see!"

Concrete poets are experimenting with new ways of communicating, with new ways of playing with language. Concrete poetry can be primarily visual or can depend basically on sounds, structure, space, or movement to convey impressions. There are many concrete poems that are impossible to pour into any single inflexible mold. Concrete poets can use any combination of space, sight, and sounds to create the effect they desire. And, of course, concrete poetry, just like other kinds of poetry, does *not* have to rhyme.

Concrete poetry can make a massive attack upon all of your senses. It can invade, plumb, and ferret out the inner and outer recesses and resources of your own mind and spirit.

Can technique such as the ones concrete poets use speak to you? say anything relevant or meaningful to you? You will have to look through this book, try some out, and discover the answer for yourself.

Enough explaining. Now it's time to immerse yourself, all of yourself, into something concrete. May you all get stuck on it, just as I did!

Concrete Is Not Always Hard

Sights
□ □ □ □

The Racers Know

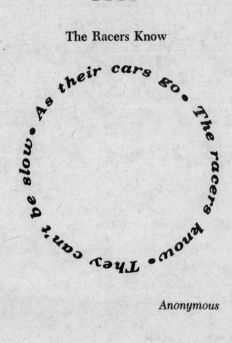

As their cars go • The racers know • They can't be slow •

Anonymous

O My!

He rocked the boat,

Did Ezra Shank;

These bubbles mark

o

o

o

o

o

o

o

Where Ezra sank.

Anonymous

I Like to Swing*

I start slow
With lazy pushes
And before I know it
I'm clear above the bushes.
Higher and higher, swing wide,
Feels like I have some wings inside!
Then up above the treetops, oh, so high!
At last I'm really sailing, sailing through the sky!

Regina Sauro

*Reprinted from the *Instructor*, © June 1958, the Instructor Publications, Inc. Used by permission.

Lazy Day

Lying

Laying

Lolling

Lulling

Doldrumming

Hohumming

Flowing

Going

Seeking

Sleeping

Slumbering

Coming

ZZZZZZZZZZZZ zzzzzzzz zzzzzzzz z

A. Barbara Pilon

Buildings*

Buildings are a great surprise,
Every one's a different size.

Offices
grow
long
and
high,
tall
enough
to
touch
the
sky.

Houses seem
more like a box,
made of glue
and building blocks.

Everytime you look, you see
Buildings shaped quite differently.

Myra Cohn Livingston

*From *Whispers and Other Poems,* © 1958 by Myra
Cohn Livingston. Reprinted by permission of Harcourt
Brace Jovanovich, Inc.

Black Ribbon of Superhighway

Black ribbon of superhighway
slices through flat, tan prairie
Glint rises on horizon
    Hums
      Roars
        Grows larger
          Streaks by
        Dwindles
    Hums
Black ribbon of superhighway slices
flat, tan prairie

Anonymous

Lollipop

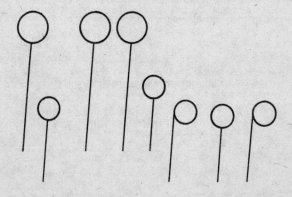

Linda Abdon

Lick Smack

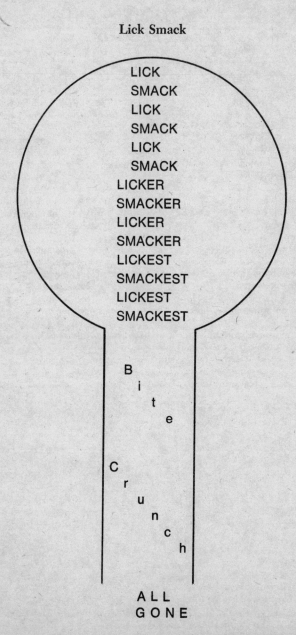

LICK
SMACK
LICK
SMACK
LICK
SMACK
LICKER
SMACKER
LICKER
SMACKER
LICKEST
SMACKEST
LICKEST
SMACKEST

B
i
t
e

C
r
u
n
c
h

A L L
G O N E

Nancy Sax Wachter

Ice Cream*

```
                    ice cream
                     i scream
                    ice cream

        bright                                  blurred
        chosen                                  rounded off
        lucent                                  made indefinite
        sharp                                       the side
                                                    nubbled
        uneven                                      syrup-slow
        curving                 the image
      but willed           the transformation          the taste
      jagged                                        glyceride
                              eating it             the memory
     silent                                         smirched
   magical, one                                     shimmering
   moment only                                      insatiable

     melting                                    accumulating,
                                             dribbling, about
     the shape itself                           the cone      to drop
     the texture                              cardboard
     a test                                     the surface
     an admission                            sticky as plastic

       the recognition          immediate    and
        deceiving the mind                unknown
         the lettering on the rim          trivial
          arguing sugar crystals,        enormous
           blatant, gummy, broken

                                          licked
        the patchwork grill              moist
         intensifying                    still

         curving                         firm
         outline                         yet
          curling its            dis-
           fingers            appear-
            around                ing
            and down
            possessing
            to draw, to take
            in the hand,
             to crunch                        Johnathan Price
             its one
             point
```

*Reprinted with permission from the December 1968 is-
sue of the *Yale Alumni Magazine*; copyright by Yale
Alumni Publications, Inc.

Apfel*

```
          pfelApfelApfelApfei
        pfelApfelApfelApfelApfelA
       felApfelApfelApfelApfelApfe
      ApfelApfelApfelApfelApfelApf
      pfelApfelApfelApfelApfelApfel
      ApfelApfelApfelApfelApfelApfe
      pfelApfelApfelApfelApfelApfelA
      ApfelApfelApfelApfelApfelApfe
      felApfelApfelApfelApfelApfel
      pfelApfelApfelApfelApfelApf
       elApfelApfelApfelWurmAp
        felApfelApfelApfelApfel
         ofelApfelApfelApfel
          felApfelApfelA
            felApfel
```

Pattern poem with an elusive intruder.

Reinhard Döhl

No. Fun

won
ton
tea
foo . . .
fie
sick
several
ate
nein
ton

A. Barbara Pilon

How to Count from 1 to 10
in Spanish in English*

Who knows
Those
Waves
What though
Sea cold
Said as they
Sedately
All chose
New wave way
Zeniths

Mason Douglas Williams

Counting One to Twenty

Yahn, Tayn, Tether, Mether, Mumph,
Hither, Lither, Auver, Dauver, Dic,
Yahndic, Tayndic, Tetherdic,
      Metherdic, Mumphit,
Yahn a mumphit, Tayn a mumphit,
Tethera mumphit, Methera mumphit,
      Jig it.

Traditional

Ounce Dice Trice*

If you get tired of counting *one, two, three,* make up your own numbers, as shepherds used to do when they had to count sheep day in, day out. You can try using these sets of words instead of numbers when you have to count to ten.

Ounce	Instant	Archery	Acreage
Dice	Distant	Butchery	Brokerage
Trice	Tryst	Treachery	Cribbage
Quartz	Catalyst	Taproom	Carthage
Quince	Quest	Tomb	Cage
Sago	Sycamore	Sermon	Sink
Serpent	Sophomore	Cinnamon	Sentiment
Oxygen	Oculist	Apron	Ointment
Nitrogen	Novelist	Nunnery	Nutmeg
Denim	Dentist	Density	Doom

Alastair Reid

*From *Ounce Dice* by Alastair Reid, by permission of Atlantic-Little, Brown and Company. Copyright © 1958.

A Number of Words*

wanton
to-do
threne
forfend
fiveling
sixain
sevenbark
aitchbone
nighness
tenet

Eve Merriam

Wan Do Tree*

wan
do
tree
fear
fife
seeks
siphon
eat
neighing
den
elephan'
twirl

Bob Cobbing

A Number of Numbers

One is a number that may be conceited,
That thinks of itself as sweet honey or jam:
For one is the number of people I am.

Two is the usual number for shoes.
Is it because one's too easy to lose?

Half circle and then a half circle again.
Though *three* feels it's boring to be so repeated,
Still, it is far better off incompleted.
For if its two halves into one whole were caught,
Then all that is three would amount to just naught.

Four makes the legs for a table or chair.
It can do the same thing for a tiger or bear.

Five is a highway going straight and then
It takes a sharp left and turns right round again.

Six is a cherry with a long stem;
In summer I eat any number of them.

Seven is the edge of a ship out at sea;
You can't see the captain, for he's taking tea.

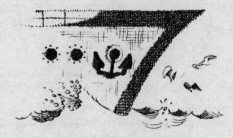

Eight is a number of which I am fond;
It goes skating in circles over the pond.
It's also a double top you can spin,
Or a very fat cat with its tail tucked in.

Nine is the full moon caught up in a tree:
Will somebody tall please release it for me?*

Eve Merriam

Pictures on the Flying Air*

A
poem
can play
with the wind
and dart and dance
and fly about in the mind
like a kite in the cloudy white
sky at so dizzy a height it
seems out of reach but
is waiting to be
very gently
pulled
down
to
the
page
below
by a
string
of
musical
words.

Scott Alexander

*Reprinted from the *Instructor*, © March 1966, the Instructor Publications, Inc. Used by permission.

Sailing to the Middle of the Bay*

Sailing to the middle of the bay,
Pushed
Along
By a sudden
 Gust of wind,
A seagull
Flew over the water
Above us,
Ex-
Tend-
Ing
Its wings to the
Full span,
Circling again
and
again above our boat,

Constantly
D
 i
  v
   i
    n
     g
For fish in the
Cold,
Deep water,
S   ng
 u   i
  r c
   fa
Each time with a prize,
Then
S   g
 o   n
  a i
   r
Back up to the heavens.

By a student of Arnold Solkov

*By a student of Arnold Solkov from "Upon First Look-ing into Christensen's Rhetoric" by Arnold Solkov, pub-lished by *English Journal.* Copyright © 1970 by the National Council of Teachers of English. Reprinted by permission of the publisher and Arnold Solkov.

Cardinal Ideograms*

0   A mouth. Can blow or breathe,
be funnel, or Hello.

1   A grass blade or a cut.

2   A question seated. And a proud
bird's neck.

3   Shallow mitten for two-fingered hand.

4   Three-cornered hut
on one stilt. Sometimes built
so the roof gapes.

5   A policeman. Polite.
Wearing visored cap.

6   O unrolling,
tape of ambiguous length
on which is written the mystery
of everything curly.

*Reprinted by permission of Charles Scribner's Sons: "Cardinal Ideograms" (copyright © 1966 May Swenson) from *Half Sun Half Sleep*.

7 A step,
   detached from its stair.

8 The universe in diagram:
   A cosmic hourglass.
   (Note enigmatic shape,
   absence of any valve of origin,
   how end overlaps beginning.)
   Unknotted like a shoelace
   and whipped back and forth,
   can serve as a model of time.

9 Lorgnette for the right eye.
   In England or if you are Alice
   the stem is on the left.

10 A grass blade or a cut
    companioned by a mouth.
    Open? Open. Shut? Shut.

May Swenson

The Drippings of a Drop

```
            ɔ
            s
           dr
          splɑ
          prinl
        drip drc
       ndribble
       rain splash
      tinkle  drip  s
     splash drop rai.
      ndrip  tinkle  slası
     ping drip sprinkle  ι
     splash drool pong drc
     tinkle drip ping sprink.
    splash drop drool poing
    ping sprinkle dribble spl
    drizzle drip splash drops
   poing sprinkle ping drool
   splash drip toing tinkles
   drool sprinkle drizzle ti
   ping tinkle splash wosh
   poing dribble bubble sι
    toing drool drip wisl
    ol splash toing pinɡ
     le sprinkle droc
       drip dr
```

Anonymous

The River

The river flows
  fast
    and
      slow
Sometimes warm
Sometimes cold
  leaves
    and
      wood
Float in the river
  on
    a
      never
        ending
        journey

Anonymous

Forsythia*

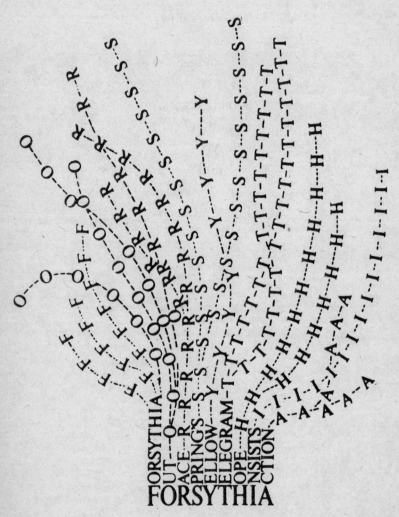

Mary Ellen Solt

*From *Concrete Poetry, A World View*, edited by Mary Ellen Solt. Indiana University Press, Bloomington (1970).

Icicle

crystal coldness
vulnerable
transparency
sharpening
itself
slowly
away

A. Barbara Pilon

Down from the Gutter

Down from the gutter they hang all day, shiny and wet they seem to say, "Hurry, get me before it's too late!"

Ilene Adams

Autumn

A
  d
    i
      z
      z
        y
          leaf
            fearfully
                        t
                          u
                            m
                              b
                                l
                                  e
                                    s
                                      to
                                        the
                                          ground.

Anonymous

Aimless*

I c i c l e

h a n g i n g

from

the

edge of the roof,

You can't fool me.

You aren't aiming at anyone.

Robert Froman

Midwinter Leaves*

A
fir
rough
against
blue snow
or a spruce
darkening the
branches of
other spruces
behind it Pines
on whitened hills
above cedar juniper
and hemlock clustered
outside a lamplit
window All of these
give over hovering or
shading after they have
been cut stood draped and
in a way made light or hung
in sparks no fire burns among
Tiers of jewels that drop
from some eye of light make
pools of color below Stain of
ruby and winking mica a starred
topaz or cold sapphires scattered
among embracing fronds extend gifts
Gems given in glistening shall endure
even now the switched-on darkness later
But eyes drop Under the asterisms
there among the aftermath of lights
showing up as shadow there is much to
be given below gems and yet beyond them
Unopened pages at the closing of the year
wide fields with tracks across them We make
our moments of fire last in this snows violet
white and in finding a kind of greenness in the
turning of white pages those ever unfallen leaves
Yes
the
old
and
new
are
adjacent not when the
summer burns but only
during the long night
From the years ground
spring stems of light

John Hollander

*From *Book World*.

In the Unroamed*

in
the
unroamed
loamed alone
of cathedral forests
where resounds the
echoing silence of the
great organ timber pipes that
tower into the crystal distance
among the cool green and
deep honey dark secret caches
of shadowed silence there grow
the christmas trees
child trees still suckling
woodmilk from beneath the moss
to lift their sapling fingers and touch
full stride their miracle
but these child trees as christmas
ornaments are severed from sanctuary
by seasoned hunters with steel saws and
shiney axes and brought to towns
priced and tagged trimmed and dragged off to
christmastreetion camps where amid
the pallor of neon and the roaring ugliness of the
christmas crash they wait for christmas
people to inspect them and select them to fit a
certain space in a certain place so much
less than a wilderness with tinsel and glass paper
and plastic trash foam and fuzz flashing lights
and icons they stand dressed to hide their slow dry dying
M
E
R
R
Y
CHRISTMAS

Mason Douglas Williams

Fir Tree Tall

Fir
tree tall
Lights glittering
Bright tinsel hung
Shimmering, glimmering
Laughter shining in the eyes
of boys
and girls
Lovely lovely
Christmas tree.

Joan Hanson

The Sand Dunes

The sand dunes looked like they had been autographed by the wind.

Pamela Swain

Showers, Clearing Later in the Day*

```
     !! !! !!      ! !       !
   !!!!!!!!! !!!! !! !!!
   !!!!!!!!!!!!!!!!!!!!!!!!!!
   !!!!!!!!!!!!!!!!!!!!!!!!!!
   !!!!!!!!!!!!!!!!!!!!!!!!!!!!        !!!!!
     !!!!!!!!! !!!!!!!!!!!
     **!!!!!!!!!!!
        !!  !  !!
        *   ! * !
          ..─* ! !  ...
            *...
               .


            *
            .
```

Eve Merriam

Restless Rushing Ceaseless Sea

Restless
rushing ceaseless sea
nervously
running in
and out
Don't you trust the land?

A. Barbara Pilon

l(a*

l(a

le
af
fa

ll

s)
one
l

iness

e. e. cummings

*© 1958 by E. E. Cummings. Reprinted from his volume, *95 Poems*, by permission of Harcourt Brace Javanovich, Inc.

Fisches Nachtgesang

Christian Morgenstern

Night Song of the Fish*

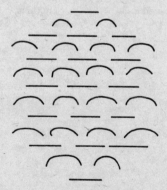

Christian Morgenstern

*English "translation" by Max Knight from *Christian Morgenstern's Galgenlieder*, University of California Press, Berkeley, California © 1963.

How Everything Happens*
(Based on a Study of the Wave)

                                        happen.
                                    to
                                up
                            stacking
                        is
                something
When nothing is happening

When it happens
                something
                        pulls
                            back
                                not
                                    to
                                        happen.

When   has happened.
        pulling back   stacking up
                happens

        has happened   stacks up.
When it   something   nothing
                        pulls back while

Then nothing is happening.

                                    happens.
                                and
                        forward
                    pushes
                up
            stacks
        something
Then

May Swenson

*Reprinted by permission of Charles Scribner's Sons: "How Everything Happens" (copyright © 1971 May Swenson) from *More Poems to Solve*.

A Dog's Life

'h   el
ta)
om   tay . eak
fetc.   .tch speak
r heei   lay down I
me sit .   play dead hee,
'h come .   er jump fetch stay u.
.k play dead sit come lay down beg stay roll over sit .
l down fetch stay beg speak jump play dead fetch hee'
s roll over jump play dead beg speak fetch heel s'
l sit beg lay down speak roll over stay d
n stay come jump sit heel fetch lay de
.it roll over speak lay down stay beg
,ed play dead come jump speak roll ov
.ed fetch jump heel play dead speak fe
ich sit stay speak jump roll over stay
peak fetch   d h play dead co
eels cor   beg lay
tay st   roll o
owns   me lay
etch roll u.   ip down sp
umped play   el play dea
tch roll ov   tay sit hee

Anonymous

A Mouse Tale: As Interpreted by Alice*

"Fury said to
a mouse, That
he met
in the
house,
'Let us
both go
to law:
I will
prosecute
you.—
Come, I'll
take no
denial;
We must
have a
trial:
For
really
this
morning
I've
nothing
to do.'
Said the
mouse to
the cur,
'Such a
trial,
dear sir,
With no
jury or
judge,
would be
wasting
our breath.'
'I'll be
judge,
I'll be
jury,'
Said
cunning
old Fury:
'I'll try
the whole
cause,
and
condemn
you
to
death.' "

Lewis Carroll

*From *Alice in Wonderland* by Lewis Carroll.

53

Supersonic Jet

SPACE INTO UPWARD QUIETLY GO WAVES SHOCK SOME

AS THE SUPERSONIC JET SWEEPS ASIDE THE AIR

LOWER AND DOWN RACING GO WAVES SHOCK SOME AND

A

BIG

BOOM

Anonymous

Why?

```
THEMTHEMTHEMTHEMTHEMT
HEMTHEMTHEMTHEMTHEMTH
EMTHEMTHEMTHEMTHEMTHE
MTHEMTHEMTHEMTHEMTHEM
THEMTHEMTHEMTHEMTHEMT
HEMTHEMTHEMTHEMTHEMTH
EMTHEMTHEMTHEMTHEMTHE
MTHEMTHEMTHEMTHEMTHEM
THEMTHEMTHEMTHEMTHEMT
HEMTHEMTHEMTHEMTHEMTH
EMTHEMTHEMTHEMTHEMTHE  ME
```

Marcïa Batteiger

Snowflakes Fall

S
n
o
w
f
l
a
k
e
s
f
a
l
l
l
o
o
k
i
n
g
for
a
p
l
a
c
e
t
o
b
e
⌐ramed.

Tish Thompson

The Grasshopper*

Down
a
deep
well
a
grasshopper
fell.
By kicking about
He thought to get out.
   He might have known better,
   For that got him wetter.
To kick round and round
Is the way to get drowned,
   And drowning is what
   I should tell you he got.
     But
     the
     well
     had
     a
     rope
     that
     dangled
     some
     hope.
And pure as molasses
On one of his passes
   He found the rope handy
   And up he went, *and he*
     it
     up
     and
     it
     up
     and
     it
     up
     and
     it
     up
     went
and hopped away proper
as any grasshopper.

David McCord

What's It All About?*

What's it all about? What's it all about? What's it all about?
it all about? What's it all about? What's it all about? What's
all about? What's it all about? What's it all about? What's it
about? What's it all about? What's it all about? What's it all
What's it all about? What's it all about? What's it all about?
it all about? What's it all about? What's it all about? What's
all about? What's it all about? What's it all about? What's it
about? What's it all about? What's it all about? What's it all
What's it all about? What's it all about? What's it all about?
it all about? What's it all about? What's it all about? What's
all about? What's it all about? What's it all about? What's it
about? What's it all about? What's it all about? What's it all
What's it all about? What's it all about? What's it all about?
it all about? What's it all about? What's it all about? What's
all about? What's it all about? What's it all about? What's it
about? What's it all about? What's it all about? What's it all
What's it all about? What's it all about? What's it all about?
it all about? What's it all about? What's it all about? What's
all about? What's it all about? What's it all about? What's it
about? What's it all about? What's it all about? What's it all
What's it all about? What's it all about? What's it all about?
it all about? What's it all about? What's it all about? What's
all about? What's it all about? What's it all about? What's it
about? What's it all about? What's it all about? What's it all
What's it all about? What's it all about? What's it all about?
it all about? What's it all about? What's it all about? What's
all about? What's it all about? What's it all about? What's it
about? What's it all about? What's it all about? What's it all
What's it all about? What's it all about? What's it all about?
it all about? What's it all about? What's it all about? What's
all about? What's it all about? What's it all about? What's it

*From *The Mason Williams Reading Matter* by Mason
Williams. Copyright © 1964, 1966, 1967, 1969 by Mason
Williams. Reprinted by permission of Doubleday & Com-
pany, Inc.

I don't know. I don't know. I don't know. I don't know. I don't
know. I don't know. I don't know. I don't know. I don't know.
I don't know. I don't know. I don't know. I don't know. I don't
know. I don't know. I don't know. I don't know. I don't know.
I don't know. I don't know. I don't know. I don't know. I don't
know. I don't know. I don't know. I don't know. I don't know.
I don't know. I don't know. I don't know. I don't know. I don't
know. I don't know. I don't know. I don't know. I don't know.
I don't know. I don't know. I don't know. I don't know. I don't
know. I don't know. I don't know. I don't know. I don't know.
I don't know. I don't know. I don't know. I don't know. I don't
know. I don't know. I don't know. I don't know. I don't know.
I don't know. I don't know. I don't know. I don't know. I don't
know. I don't know. I don't know. I don't know. I don't know.
I don't know. I don't know. I don't know. I don't know. I don't
know. I don't know. I don't know. I don't know. I don't know.
I don't know. I don't know. I don't know. I don't know. I don't
know. I don't know. I don't know. I don't know. I don't know.
I don't know. I don't know. I don't know. I don't know. I don't
know. I don't know. I don't know. I don't know. I don't know.
I don't know. I don't know. I don't know. I don't know. I don't
know. I don't know. I don't know. I don't know. I don't know.
I don't know. I don't know. I don't know. I don't know. I don't
know. I don't know. I don't know. I don't know. I don't know.
I don't know. I don't know. I don't know. I don't know. I don't
know. I don't know. I don't know. I don't know. I don't know.
I don't know. I don't know. I don't know. I don't know. I don't
know. I don't know. I don't know. I don't know. I don't know.
I don't know. I don't know. I don't know. I don't know. I don't

Mason Douglas Williams

Diamond Cut Diamond*

Two cats
One up a tree
One under a tree
The cat up a tree is he
The cat under the tree is she
The tree is witch elm, just incidentally.
He takes no notice of she, she takes no notice of he.
He stares at the wooly clouds passing, she stares at the tree.
There's been a lot written about cats, by Old Possum, Yeats and Company
But not Alfred de Musset or Lord Tennyson or Poe or anybody
Wrote about one cat under, and one cat up, a tree
God knows why this should be left for me
Except I like cats as cats be
Especially one cat up
And one cat under
A witch elm
Tree.

Ewart Milne

*From *Diamond Cut Diamond* by Ewart Milne. The Bodley Head, Ltd.

Like Attracts Like*

like   attracts   like

like   attracts   like

like   attracts   like

like   attracts   like

like   attracts   like

like   attracts   like

like attracts like

likeattractslike

likeattractlike

likattraclike

likttradike

littralike

littdikts

Emmett Williams

Individualista*

Ladislav Novak

*From *Concrete Poetry*, A World View, edited by Mary Ellen Solt. Indiana University Press, Bloomington (1970).

Mirror*

When you look
into a mirror
it is not
yourself you see,
but a kind
of apish error
posed in fearful
symmetry.

John Updike

*From *The Carpentered Hen and Other Tame Creatures* by John Updike. Copyright © 1957 by John Updike. By permission of Harper & Row, Publishers, Inc.

Ubiquity

ub
  ib
    ubibubib
    ubibubibubib
    ubibubibubibubib
       qui? qui? qui? qui?
  uiuiuiui . . .
ubuibiubuibiubiibuubiibu qui???
          qt? qt? qt?
     quit quit quit
      i quit
      u quit
       u quit
       i quit
 y? y? y? y? y? y? y? y? y? y?
    too much
   u i u i u i u i u i u i u i
    too much
ubiquity ubiquity ubiquity ubiquity u b qui?

This poem presents the problems of overpopulation and the loss of individuality which confront human beings who are living today. Using the letters in the word "ubiquity," the problems are stated and one solution to the dilemma is offered.

To "read" and understand this poem, many of the letters need to be spoken individually.

A. Barbara Pilon

Star*

star

star

star

star

star

star

star

star

star

star

star

star

steer

Ian Hamilton Finlay

"There are so many stars—which single star shall we choose to steer by?
The poem presents in an undidactic
way the ideas of clarity, resolution,
and choice."   (I.H.F.)

Night Practice*

I
will
remember
with my breath
to make a mountain,
with my sucked-in breath
a valley, with my pushed-out
breath a mountain. I will make
a valley wider than the whisper, I
will make a higher mountain than the cry;
will with my will breathe a mountain, I will
with my will breathe a valley. I will push out
a mountain, suck in a valley, deeper than the shout
you must die, harder, heavier, sharper, a mountain than
the truth *you must die.* I will remember. My breath will
make a mountain. My will will remember to will. I suck-
ing, pushing, I will breathe a valley, I will breathe a mountain.

May Swenson

Life: From Beginning to End

BIRTH

THUMB

KINDERGARTEN

C
ADOLESCENCE
N
F   T
U   E
S N D E R S T A   E
I   A N   S
O   D
N   I N G

MORE
NEEDED
                W
    ADULTHOOD   O
                R
                R
                BILLS
                E
                S

DEATH
    H   N
    END?   O
                        B E G I N N I N G
            THE B E G I N N I N G

Peter Quinn

Please

please

SKY

ᴚ HTRAƎ Ɐ EARTH
C O N S E R V E
WATER

Sam McDonald

Nix*

NIX   **ONIX**   **ONIXO**
If only we could
Nix   on
and then
Nix   off

N   O   X   O   N   I
  X   N   O
I   N   I   N   N   X

        X   O   N
        N   I   X
        O   I   N

                    x   n   x
                    o   x   o
                    i   x   n

                              x   n   x
                              i   x   i
                              x   o   x

Eve Merriam

Fooling Around with Words

□ □ □ □ □ □ □ □ □ □ □ □ □ □ □ □ □

Orchestra

flag

Patsy Jones

Peace

Peace
clock
people

David Heeb

Exit

Alyson Davis

Money

$MON.EY
Record

Jay Evans

Vase

Jail

Pencil

Wig

Devil

Pig

Cow

fish

Seal

Smile

Teacher

Loop

microSCOPE

Indian

Beth Gaunt

Boredom

boredommmmmmmmmmmmmm
carelss
i   solated

A. Barbara Pilon

Voracious

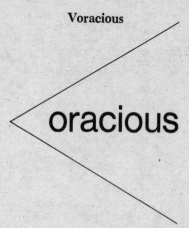

oracious

Diane Scott

Rubber

R U B B E R

BAND

Rebecca L. Ayers

Chair

chair

birthday

a c c e l e r a t e

Bob Evans

School Is*

School is a

wandering
figment of
the imagin
ation

purposelessly

around

from class room

to class room

I

repeat:

school is a
figment of
the imag
ination

it makes a lovely

chorus for a

horrible

horrible song

school is a
figment of
the imagin
ation

and besides that it's beginning to be true.

Ha!

Michaele Lundberg

Ubiquity*

ubiquityubiquityubiquityubiquityubiquityubiquityubiquityubiquity
ubiquityubiquityubiquityubiquityubiquityubiquityubiquityubiquity
ubiquityubiquityubiquityubiquityubiquityubiquityubiquityubiquity
ubiquityubiquityubiquityubiquityubiquityubiquityubiquityubiquity
ubiquityubiquityubiquityubiquityubiquityubiquityubiquityubiquity
ubiquityubiquityubiquityubiquityubiquityubiquityubiquityubiquity
ubiquityubiquityubiquityubiquityubiquityubiquityubiquityubiquity
ubiquityubiquityubiquityubiquityubiquityubiquityubiquityubiquity
ubiquityubiquityubiquityubiquityubiquityubiquityubiquityubiquity
ubiquityubiquityubiquityubiquityubiquityubiquityubiquityubiquity
ubiquityubiquityubiquityubiquityubiquityubiquityubiquityubiquity
ubiquityubiquityubiquityubiquityubiquityubiquityubiquityubiquity
ubiquityubiquityubiquityubiquityubiquityubiquityubiquityubiquity
ubiquityubiquityubiquityubiquityubiquityubiquityubiquityubiquity
ubiquityubiquityubiquityubiquityubiquityubiquityubiquityubiquity
ubiquityubiquityubiquityubiquityubiquityubiquityubiquityubiquity
ubiquityubiquityubiquityubiquityubiquityubiquityubiquityubiquity
ubiquityubiquityubiquityubiquityubiquityubiquityubiquityubiquity
ubiquityubiquityubiquityubiquityubiquityubiquityubiquityubiquity
ubiquityubiquityubiquityubiquityubiquityubiquityubiquityubiquity
ubiquityubiquityubiquityubiquityubiquityubiquityubiquityubiquity
ubiquityubiquityubiquityubiquityubiquityubiquityubiquityubiquity
ubiquityubiquityubiquityubiquityubiquityubiquityubiquityubiquity
ubiquityubiquityubiquityubiquityubiquityubiquityubiquityubiquity
ubiquityubiquityubiquityubiquityubiquityubiquityubiquityubiquity
ubiquityubiquityubiquityubiquityubiquityubiquityubiquityubiquity
ubiquityubiquityubiquityubiquityubiquityubiquityubiquityubiquity
ubiquityubiquityubiquityubiquityubiquityubiquityubiquitvubiquity
ubiquityubiquityubiquityubiquityubiquityubiquityubiquityubiquity
ubiquityubiquityubiquityubiquityubiquityubiquityubiquityubiquity
ubiquityubiquityubiquityubiquitvubiquityubiquityubiquityubiquity
ubiquityubiquityubiquityubiquityubiquityubiquityubiquityubiquity
ubiquityubiquityubiquityubiquityubiquityubiquityubiquityubiquity
ubiquityubiquityubiquityubiquityubiquityubiquityubiquityubiquity
ubiquityubiquityubiquityubiquityubiquityubiquityubiquityubiquity
ubiquitvubiquityubiquityubiquityubiquityubiquityubiquityubiquity
ubiquityubiquityubiquityubiquityubiquityubiquityubiquityubiquity
ubiquityubiquityubiquityubiquityubiquityubiquityubiquityubiquity
ubiquityubiquityubiquityubiquityubiquityubiquityubiquityubiquity

Bob Stewart

*The author points out that to be effective this poem
should appear on every page of this book.

Tackle

Rick Eckstein

Sounds
□ □ □ □ □

Teacher

Tch   Tch   Tch   Tch   Tch
Tch   Tch   Tch   Tch   Tch

A. Barbara Pilon

Of Rounds*

MOON
     round
          goes around while going around a
                        round
                             EARTH.

EARTH
    round
        with MOON
               round
                   going around while going around,
goes around while going around a
                  round
                     SUN.

SUN
   round
      with EARTH
           round
              with MOON
                  round
                     going around while going
around, and MERCURY
              round
            and VENUS
                round
                   going around while
going around, and MARS
          round
            with two MOONS
                     round
                     round
                       going around
while going around, and JUPITER
             round
              with twelve MOONS
                        round
                        round
                        round
                        round
                        round
                        round
                        round
                        round
                        round
                        round
                        round
                        round

going around while going around, and SATURN
                                        round
                                                with nine
MOONS
        round
        round
        round
        round
        round
        round
        round
        round
        round
            going around while going around, and URANUS
                                                    round
with five MOONS
                round
                round
                round
                round
                round
                going around while going around, and NEPTUNE
round
        with two MOONS
                        round
                        round
                            going around while going around, and
PLUTO
        round
            going around while going around, goes around while
going around
                A   **   OF ROUNDS
                    *****   Round
                  ** * **
                    ** * **
                  *   *   *
                    * * *
                  *   *   *
                    *   *
                        *

Major layout of asterisks forming a spiral pattern

May Swenson

The Dirty Word*

swallow it raw

awr

rwa

arw

rwa

WAR

Eve Merriam

Ways of Winding a Watch (Number 1)*

a little forward
a little back
a little forward
a little back
a little forward

a little back
a little bored don't be
you've got to keep going
back a little for
ward a lit a back a for
a bac   kthere!

Eve Merriam

Spaces
□ □ □ □

The Hippopotamus*

What fun	to be
A Hippo	-potamus
And weigh	a ton
From top	to bottamus

Michael Flanders

*From *Creatures Great and Small* by Michael Flanders. Copyright © 1964 by Michael Flanders. Reprinted by permission of Holt, Rinehart and Winston, Inc.

His Thinking on Anything

A. Barbara Pilon

Little Calendar*

April	light	light	light	light
May	light	trees	light	trees
June	trees	light	trees	light
July	trees	trees	trees	trees
August	trees'	light	trees'	light
September	lights	trees	lights	trees

Ian Hamilton Finlay

Lullaby*

light	dark	light	dark	light	dark
hot	night	hot	night	hot	
must	get	sleep		must	sleep
BAR		BAR		BAR	
red	bed	red	bed	red	bed
beer	can	kicked		beer	can
can't	sleep	can't	sleep	can't	
car		car		car	
heels	click	heels	click	heels	click
one	two	kick		she	screams
she	screams	dog	barks	dog	barks
BAR		BAR		beer	can
can't	sleep	can't	sleep	can't	
hot	night	hot	night	hot	
red	bed	red	bed	red	bed
BAR		BAR		BAR	
BAR		BAR			

Richard J. Margolis

Sleep*

Sleep	like a log	lie	sleep	to sleep
fall	like a stone	fall	to fall	to sleep
lie	like a rug	sleep	to lie	to sleep
log		tree	chair	to sleep
stone		river	garden	to sleep
rug			walk	to sleep
body	immerse	sleep	sleep	to sleep
condition	motionless	sleep	sleep	to sleep
interval	inactive	sleep	sleep	to sleep

Larry Freifeld

Life Cycle

l

l i

 l i f

  l i f e

 l i f

l i

l

A. Barbara Pilon

Take Your Choice

□ □ □ □ □ □ □ □ □ □ □

Atonement

At

ONE

ment

Judith White Arthur

Acrobats*

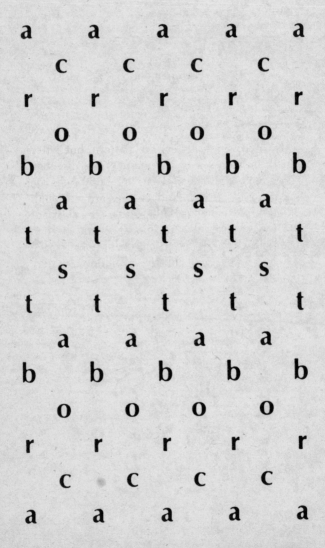

Ian Hamilton Finlay

←————————

"Isolated, single letters are pattern, but letters joined in words (as these are) are direction. Those in the 'acrobats' poem are both, behaving like the real circus acrobats who are now individual units, now springing together—diagonals and towers. Properly, the poem should be constructed of cut-out letters, to occupy not a page but an entire wall above a children's playground." (I. A. H.)

Crossing*

STOP LOOK LISTEN
as gate stripes swing down,
count the cars hauling distance
upgrade through town:
warning whistle, bellclang,
engine eating steam,
engineer waving,
a fast-freight dream:
B&M boxcar,
boxcar again,
Frisco gondola,
eight-nine-ten
Erie and Wabash,
Seaboard, U.P.,
Pennsy tankcar,
twenty-two, three,
Phoebe Snow, B&O,
thirty-four, five,
Santa Fe cattle
shipped alive,
red cars, yellow cars,
orange cars, black,
Youngstown steel
down to Mobile
on Rock Island track,

*From *Letter from a Distant Land* by Philip Booth.
Copyright 1953 by Philip Booth. First appeared in *The
New Yorker*. Reprinted by permission of The Viking
Press, Inc.

fifty-nine, sixty,
hoppers of coke,
Anaconda copper,
hotbox smoke,
eighty-eight,
red-ball freight,
Rio Grande,
Nickel Plate,
Hiawatha,
Lackawanna,
rolling fast
and loose,
ninety-seven,
coal car,
boxcar,
CABOOSE!

Philip Booth

Ping-Pong

ping pong*
    ping pong ping
    pong ping pong
        ping pong

Eugen Gomringer

*From *Concrete Poetry, A World View*, by Mary Ellen Solt. Indiana University Press, Bloomington (1970).

Silencio*

silencio silencio silencio
silencio silencio silencio
silencio   silencio
silencio silencio silencio
silencio silencio silencio

Eugen Gomringer

*From *Concrete Poetry, A World View*, edited by Mary Ellen Solt, Indiana University Press, Bloomington (1970).

For You to Try
□ □ □ □ □ □ □ □ □

Tulip

Tulip
Tall, Cuppish
For tiptoeing through
For planting in yards
Tiny Tim
Yellow
Blue
Red
Pink
Tulip
Tu
Two
ips
Lips
Kiss

David Kleiman

Editor's note: If you would like to try this "flor-
poetica" type of concrete poetry—a term coined
by David Kleiman—here is the form David in-
vented and followed for his poem:

Florpoetica

Flower
Description
Prepositional phrase
Prepositional phrase
Association
Color
Color
Color
Color
Flower
First part of the name
New part for it
Second part of the name
New part for it
New name

David Kleiman

Constantly Risking Absurdity*

Constantly risking absurdity
                              and death
          whenever he performs
                         above the heads
                                   of his audience
          the poet like an acrobat
                         climbs on rime
                                   to a high wire of his own making
and balancing on eyebeams
                                   above a sea of faces
               paces his way
                         to the other side of day
          performing entrechats
                              and sleight-of-foot tricks
and other high theatrics
                         and all without mistaking
               any thing
                         for what it may not be
          For he's the super realist
                                   who must perforce perceive
               taut truth
                              before the taking of each stance or step
in his supposed advance
                                   toward that still higher perch
          where Beauty stands and waits
                              with gravity
                                        to start her death-defying leap

And he
>a little charleychaplin man
>>who may or may not catch
>her fair eternal form
>>>spreadeagled in the empty air
>>of existence

Lawrence Ferlinghetti

Editor's note: The way this poem is arranged is quite representative of Lawrence Ferlinghetti's works. However, in "Constantly Risking Absurdity," the word arrangement seems most appropriate for the idea the poet has expressed in this particular piece. Do you think you could rewrite his poem in a way that would heighten even more the idea that a poet is like an acrobat?

Some Words for You to Play with Concretely .

narrow	monotony
egotistical	shock
noise	invisible
bicycle	joy
cancer	downhill
amnesia	melt
pain	pipe
full	cross
balloon	needle
rocket	egg
rough	fractionated
dollars	cat
crowd	giraffe
slant	camel
zero	snake
square	dandelion
hugged	impaled

What other words can you think of to illustrate their meanings concretely?

The Beginning